DISCOVERY OF THE SQUARE

BRUNO MUNARI

GEORGE WITTENBORN INC.
1018 MADISON AVENUE, NEW YORK 21, N.Y.

The square is as high and as wide as a man with his arms outstretched. In the most ancient writings, and in the rock inscriptions of early man, it signifies the idea of enclosure, of house, of settlement.

Enigmatic in its simplicity, in the monotonous repetition of four equal sides and four equal angles, it creates a series of interesting figures: a whole group of harmonic rectangles, the golden section, and the logarithmic spiral, which also occurs in nature in the organic growth of plants and in parts of animals.

With its structural possibilities it has helped artists and architects of all epochs and styles by giving them a harmonic skeleton on which to build an artistic construction. It is therefore present in all styles of all peoples in all periods, both as a structural element and as a surface to support and determine a particular form of decoration. It is static if it stands on its side and dynamic if it stands on an angle. It is magic if filled with numbers, and it can also be diabolic and satanic if these numbers maintain their relationship no matter whether they are squared or cubed. It is found in nature in many minerals. According to Peano it is a curve. It can be transformed into triangles or rectangles simply by appropriate cuts and rearrangements. In ancient times it had the power of warding off plagues. It has given form both to famous ancient cities and to modern buildings: Babylon, Tell el Amarna, the Parthenon, the Arch of Septimius Severus, the Duomo of Pisa, Palazzo Farnese, Le Corbusier's museum of unlimited extendability... The bays of the portico of Brunelleschi's Foundling Hospital are square. In the ground-plans of many churches the square area below is the most logical answer to the hemispherical dome above, just as a square photograph corresponds, with the minimum distortion or waste, to the round lens of the camera. Phidias used a square form for his lacunaria. At Olympia, the Palestra, the Theocoleon, the Leonidaeum and other buildings had square ground plans...

Many ancient games still in use today are based on the square: chess, checkers, the fifteen puzzle with its ten trillion possible combinations, dice, even puss in the corner... And the cowboy square dances are famous.

In the Eastern Chin dynasty it gave the Chinese written character its square form. It has given structure to the letters of our own, of the Hebrew and other alphabets. All over the world, a small square of linen is a handkerchief. Two squares of matting are the basic unit of the traditional Japanese house. Twenty-eight squares cover the surface of a brick. According to an old Chinese saying the infinite is a square without angles.

" The square is the purest form of a spatial idea complete in itself. It represents one of the orders of pregnant spiritual symbolism. All other rectangles are squares which depart from the norm by the extension of height or width. "

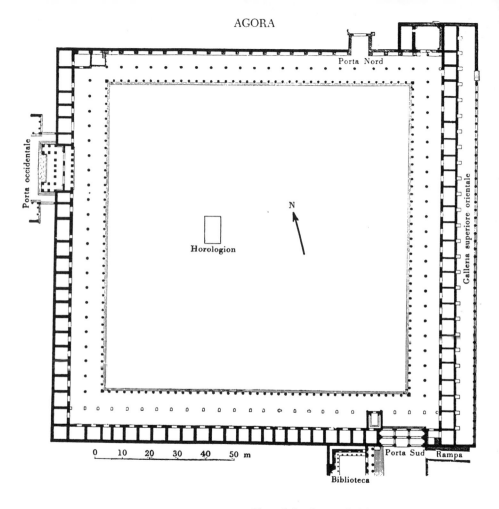

AGORA

Porta Nord

Porta occidentale

Galleria superiore orientale

N

Horologion

0   10   20   30   40   50 m

Porta Sud   Rampa

Biblioteca

Plan of the Agora of Ephesus, Hellenistic age.

JOSEF ALBERS

Homage to the twilight square, 1951.

AAGARD ANDERSEN

Design in black and white on an area of 48 squares.

THE ALTAR OF BURNT OFFERING

" And thou shalt make an altar of shittim wood, five cubits long, and five cubits broad : the altar shall be foursquare... " - Exodus xxvii. 1.

8

ANAGUTA

Characters from American petroglyphs at Anagutà.

ANCIENT EGYPT

Art, in ancient Egypt, was based on geometry and the fixed rules of a canon. The basis of this system was the square. Since the time of the Old Kingdom, as may be

seen in the tomb of King Zoser of the third dynasty, at Sakkara, artists who had a wall

to decorate divided it up into squares so as to be able to calculate the proportions. Traces of similar grid-lines have also been found in other tombs at Sakkara, and in tombs of the New Kingdom at Thebes. In sculpture the square form inspired the so-called "cubic" statue in which the human figure, generally a person of rank, is disposed in such a way that it remains within the co-ordinates of a cube. A typical example is the statue of the architect Senmut of the eighteenth dynasty, in the Cairo Museum.

The square is the basis of the pyramid and, in Gnostic times, mystical and symbolical interpretations in connection with this geometric shape were disseminated. In fact, the square with its four sides, was regarded as the symbol of the four elements and thus of "materiality", subordinate to the form of the triangle, whose three sides symbolized the spirit, and also represented, schematically, the rising flame: *pyra*, fire, whence "*pyramid*".

THE KITE

A box-kite of two simple cells.

THE ROMAN ARCH

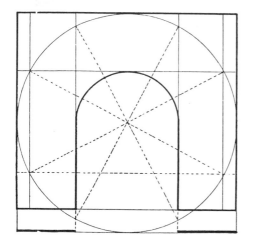

Proportions of the Arch of Septimius Severus.

MAYAN ARCHITECTURE

Detail of a frieze of the temple of Uxmal in Yucatán. All Mayan buildings are based on mathematical laws, on precise forms and proportions.

BABYLON

Babylon is a square city, says Herodotus, and every side measures one hundred and twenty stadia. The city is full of three- or four-story houses, and is traversed by straight parallel streets perpendicular to the river. It is also divided into two parts: in one part is the Royal Palace, and in the other part the bronze-doored sanctuary of Bel, the Babylonian Zeus, two stadia square. In the middle of the sanctuary a massive tower rises on a square base, each side of which measures one stadium. This tower supports other towers, one on top of the other in decreasing order, eight in all. On the last tower there is a great temple and in it there is an elaborately ornamented bed with a gold table beside it. No deity and no human being lives in this place, except the woman chosen by the god.

A - MIOM

Brahmin character. Phonetic value: ba. The same sign has, in Korean, the phonetic value: miom.

BET

Egyptian hieroglyphs. Phonetic value: bet.

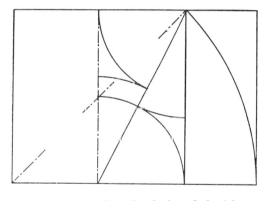

Proportions of a Greek bas-relief. Athens.

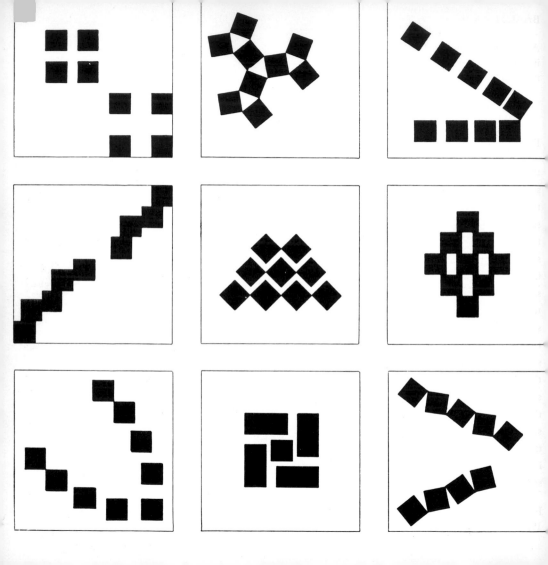

BAAL-SHAMIN

Axonometric view of the monumental buildings of the Temple of Baal-shamin at Palmyra (reconstructed).

BELLOLI

the field

square

the square

square

the city

square

the prison

square

the tomb

square

the tent

square

the skin

square

the pupil

square

the square

is

society.

From poems on elementary geometry, Basle 1959.

THE BAUHAUS

Experiments with different groupings of nine squares. The Bauhaus, Weimar.

MAX BILL

Monument to the Unknown Political Prisoner, 1952.

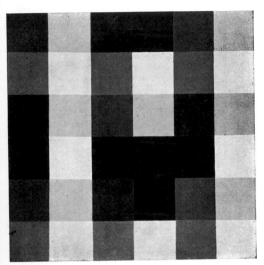

Field with eight groups, 1956.

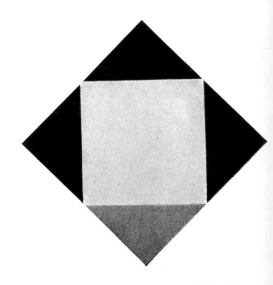

White element, oil on canvas, 68 by 68 cm. (26 ¾ by 26 ¾ in.), diagonal.

MOUTH

Chinese ideogram meaning " mouth ".

HOUSE

The word "house" in Sumerian ideographic writing.

MASUZAWA'S HOUSE

The house of the architect Masuzawa in Tokyo, 1952.

GOTHIC CATHEDRAL

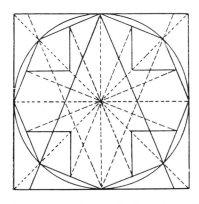

Proportions of the Cathedral of Chalons-sur-Marne. Cross-section.

ELECTRONIC BRAIN

THE CHURCH OF SANTA SOPHIA

Santa Sophia, Constantinople. The plan consists of rectangles of proportions $1 : \sqrt{2}$ arranged around a central area which is very nearly a square.

THE CHURCH OF SAN LORENZO

The church of San Lorenzo in Turin, by Guarino Guarini. The whole composition is based on a square divided in turn into squares and golden rectangles.

FIVE TIMES

Given a square, describe another square five times larger.

SHELLS

The organic growth of many shells follows the curve of the logarithmic spiral, which derives from the square.

COMPOSITIONS

Composition with four squares.

CONCAVE CONVEX

Composition with eight squares.

Form obtained by bending a square of wire gauze until the corners touch at pre-established points on the surface. The explanatory diagrams show the various stages in the production of the final form. The points of anchorage are established on the surface of the square according to harmonic

roportions. These wire gauzes, so curved
nd hung from the ceiling of a room, may
e used to decorate a wall, their mobile
nd transparent shadows giving a fish-net ef-
ect. Munari, 1948.

21

SOLAR ENERGY CONCENTRATOR

The above concentrator is used in America to harness solar energy. It consists of 180 adjustable mirrors, each about 50 cm. square.

AGAINST THE PLAGUE

In ancient times the square was believed to have magical properties including power to prevent plague, and it was common practice to wear a silver disk, with a square cut in it, on a necklace.

ROMANESQUE CROSS

Notre-Dame-du-Port, Clermont-Ferrand, eleventh century.

CRETE

Characters from a Minoan inscription, Crete.

The distortion of a flat square produces these roofs in the shape of a hyperbolic paraboloid. The form of the roof varies according to how the four basic elements are joined.

23

PEANO'S CURVE

One of the cardinal principles of geometry is that a point has no dimensions and that a curve has one only and therefore can never fill an area. This is another firm conviction that has been badly shaken—by the " curve of Peano ", which belongs to the supreme type of pathological curves and does fill up an area. It can occupy not only the entire inside of a square but also climb into the space of a complete cubic box. The successive stages of this curve may be seen in the following figures:

1

2

3

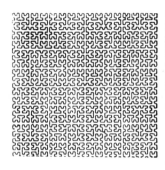

Take any point in a square or cube. It can be demonstrated that the curve, when completed, will pass through this point. And since the same reasoning may be applied to any other point, the logical conclusion is that the curve must fill the whole of the square or cube. Mathematicians once held that every curve must, of necessity, have tangents, because, they said, this property is axiomatic. But now, in 1890, Peano, to their great amazement, had devised a curve that would not admit tangents at any point, a curve that filled the entire area of a square, and for that reason could only be re-

presented by a square black patch. Since then curves without tangents have become familiar to mathematicians.

CHECKERS

Checker players in the open air at Bournemouth.

24

ISLAMIC DECORATION

Islamic mural decoration of the thirteenth century.

DIAGONAL

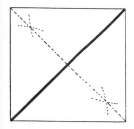

Given the diagonal, construct the square.

DIAGONALS

The diagonals of these two figures are equal.

DIATOM

Microscopic algae are of various forms, including the square.

26

DISTORTIONS

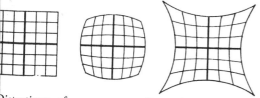

Distortions of a square surface, the two medians remaining constant.

DOUBLING

The problem of doubling the square was easily solved by the Greeks, by constructing a second square on the diagonal of the first. But this raised another problem: the doubling of the cube. Working on this problem Menelaus of Alexandria tried in vain to solve it with a construction of straight lines and arcs of circles and with other curves. After much work, instead of getting the double of the cube, he discovered the ellipse, parabola and hyperbola.

ALBRECHT DÜRER

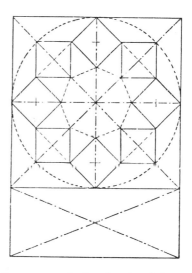

Proportions of the church of Santa Maria degli Angeli, Rome, after Dürer.

DOUBLE, TRIPLE

Given a square, describe its double, triple, quadruple, quintuple, etc.

27

INTERNAL DIVISIONS

Division of a square into two rectangles at points determined by various combinations of arcs and lines derived from the dimensions of the square itself.

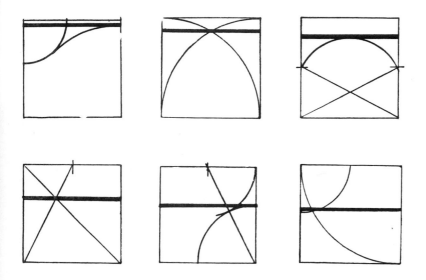

THE DUOMO OF PISA

Proportions of the façade of the Duomo of Pisa.

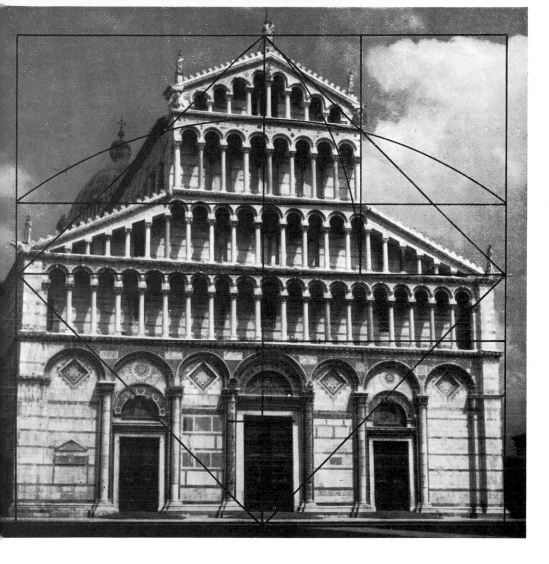

GOD OF THE TEMPEST

The Temple of the God of the Tempest at Carchemish. The sanctuary of the temple was a perfect square.

HEXAGON

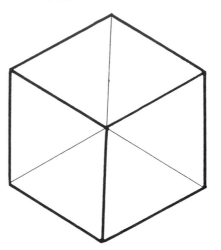

The projection of a cube with two opposite corners in line is a hexagon.

VAN DOESBURG

Arithmetical composition, 1930.

IVORY LABELS

Ivory labels with numerical markings, found in the royal tomb attributed to Menes, founder of the first dynasty, at Nagada in Egypt.

EUCLID

The square circumscribing a given circle has twice the area of the square inscribed in the same circle.

FAUTRIER

The Empty Box, painting, 1954.

SQUARE HANDKERCHIEF

A scene from Verdi's *Othello*.

IRON

In a mass of molten iron, the transformation from liquid to solid, on cooling, comes about by the formation of crystalloid nuclei in the form of cubes (as may be seen in a series of microphotographs) which multiply rapidly along crystallographic axes until the whole mass is filled.

TRENCH

Character used in writings of the Bamum (a tribe of the Cameroons) to indicate "trench". Similar characters are also to be found in ancient Sinaitic writings.

FORMS DERIVED FROM THE SQUARE

Two-dimensional compositions derived from combining, rotating or modifying square surfaces.

FLUORITE

Rectangular structure of fluorite crystals.

WINDMILL

Four cuts along the diagonals of a square of cardboard make this simple toy.

The gardens of the Villa Medici, on the Pincio, in Rome. Architect: Annibale Lippi.

SUNFLOWER

The arrangement of the seeds of the sunflower follows the logarithmic spiral.

GAMES

Chess, checkers, dominoes, puss in the corner, are among the games derived from the square.

THE 15 PUZZLE

The 15 Puzzle, as its inventor Sam Lloyd called it in 1878, was a great success. Employers had to put up notices forbidding their employees to play the game during working hours, under pain of dismissal. A French journalist of the time described it as more harmful than tobacco or alcohol, responsaible for migraine, neuralgia and neuroses.

Enormous prizes were offered for the solution of apparently simple problems, but nobody ever won them. The 15 numbers and the one empty space may theoretically be arranged in the box in 20,922,-789,888,000 different ways.

But two American mathematicians, Johnson and Story, proved that, starting from any given position, and pushing the numbers around in the box, only half of the total number of possible positions may be reached. This meant that if there were ten trillion positions that could be reached, there were ten trillion more that could not.

And the fact that half the starting positions in the puzzle were incapable of solution explains why the generous prizes were never won, for it always happened that the prize contests involved one of these impossible positions.

GRADATIONS IN TEXTURE

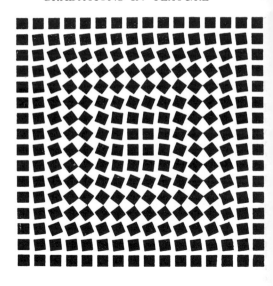

Gradations in texture obtained by distorting the squares in a chequered pattern.
Ulm School, 1957.

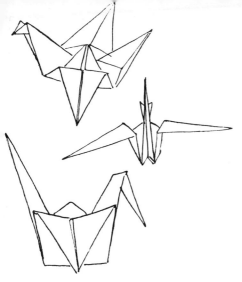

make public the theory of incommensurables, perished in a shipwreck because, according to the legend, the inexpressible and the unimaginable should have remained hidden for all time. So the man, whose crime was that he had unwittingly revealed one of the secrets of nature, was sent back to his place of origin to remain lashed by the waves for ever.

It is probable that the legend grew out of a very real resentment against the revealing of results, particularly to outsiders, which were certainly very embarrassing in that they demonstrated the error of the Pythagorean conception of the point. After this discovery, in fact, a revision of the fundamental concepts of geometry began take place, leading to the celebrated sophsophisms of Zeno, and eventually to the Elements of Euclid.

GOTHIC

Ornamental Gothic motifs.

JAPANESE TOYS

Numerous toys can be made by the Japanese game of folding a square of paper in various ways. Famous examples are a bird which moves its wings, a foldable box, an object in the shape of four hollow pyramids, upside down and joined together, into which one can put four fingers.

INCOMMENSURABLES

Notwithstanding the Pythagorean conception of the extended point, incommensurables, i.e. quantities that have no common measure, exist. It seems that the discovery of the incommensurability between the side and the diagonal of the square was made by Hippasus of Metapontum, a disciple of Pythagoras, who, having been the first to

HOMO QUADRATUS

MAX HUBER

Composition on a square basis.

In the theory of Homo Quadratus, number, first principle of the universe, acquires symbolic significance, founded on a series of numerical correspondences which are also aesthetic correspondences. The earliest forms of the theory related to music. The musical tones are eight, observed an unknown Carthusian monk, because four were discovered by the ancients and four were added by the moderns (he was referring to the four authentic modes and the four plagal modes). For other writers, and in popular belief, the number four was a key number of great efficacy, a fertile procreator of series. There are four cardinal points, four principal winds, four phases of the moon, four seasons; four is the constitutive number of Timaeus' tetrahedral corpuscles of fire, and there are four letters in the name ADAM. And four, too, as Vitruvius teaches, is the number of man, since the width of a man with his arms outstretched corresponds to his height, thus forming the base and height of an ideal square; and four is the number of moral perfection, for the man who is morally fortified stands four-square against attack.

PHOTOGRAPHIC COMPOSITION
by Max Huber

OPTICAL ILLUSIONS

Optical illusions of Hering (or Helmholtz) on square areas.

ROMANESQUE INITIALS

From a twelfth-century manuscript.

CUBIC LAMP

The shape of this lamp, contained within a cube, allows easy assembly and dismantling by means of the two diagonal metal supports. The simple design makes it very inexpensive to produce.

KARL GERSTNER

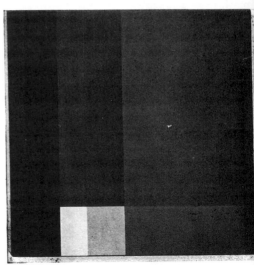

Blue-yellow sequence on red, 1958-59.

THE INFINITE

"The infinite is a square—without corners."
Ancient Chinese saying.

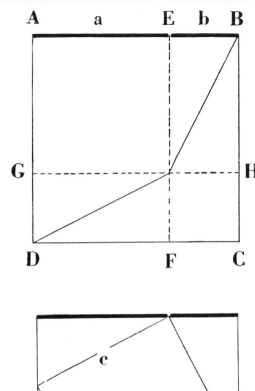

THE CHINESE AND PYTHAGORAS

About five centuries before Pythagoras, the Chinese knew about the relation between the sides of a right-angled triangle. The proof, found in the "Book of King Chu-Pei-Tsuan", does not actually demonstrate the theorem of Pythagoras, but one closely allied to it.

Let a and b be the two sides of a right-angled triangle (the sides about the right angle). Place one after the other in a straight line. With this line as base, constuct the square ABCD. Mark the point of contact of the two segments a and b on all four sides of the square, at E, F, G and H, as shown in the figure. Join EF and GH so that the square ABCD is now divided into an area that is the square of a, an area that is the square of b, and two rectangles each of area ab. Divide each of these two rectangles diagonally, and we have four equal right-angled triangles with hypotenuse c.

Place the four right-angled triangles on the area ABCD so that the right angles of the triangles coincide with the right angles of the square, and we obtain an area in the middle of which is the square on the hypotenuse c.

KLEE

Studies in squares by Klee.

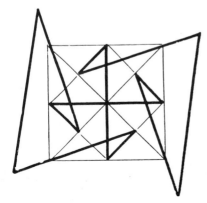

Dynamic exfoliation of a given static.

LE CORBUSIER

Museum of unlimited extendability, seen from above. Built on piles with entrance from the central court. Infinite possibilities of internal arrangement with prefabricated units.

MAZES

Plans of mazes in Italian villa gardens of the seventeenth century.

42

LEONARDO

Study of the proportions of the human figure, enclosed in a square.

Those adept in Egyptian priesthood considered the square as the expression of man, in that man, in an upright position with arms outstretched was found to be of equal measure in height and width.

LEONARDO

Proportions of a profile.

GREEK FRET

VERENA LOEWENSBERG

Composition 257, 1956-57.

THE EIGHT QUEENS

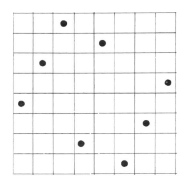

Problem: place eight queens on an ordinary chessboard of sixty-four squares in such a way that none is in check from any of the others. It was proposed by Nauck in 1850 and solved by him, and by various others later. Ninety-two solutions are possible. Here are two of them, the second of which is symmetrical, i.e. it remains unchanged if the board is turned through 180 degrees.

RICHARD P. LOHSE

Horizontal divisions, 1949-53.

KAZIMIR MALEVICH

" When in 1913, in my desperate attempt to liberate art from the useless burden of the object, I sought refuge in the form of the square, and exhibited a picture that represented nothing but a black square on a white ground, the critics did not like it; nor did the public: ' All that we loved has been lost, we are now in the desert. Before us there is nothing but a black square on a white ground '. The perfect square seemed to both critics and public something incomprehensible and menacing—which is what one might have expected.

The ascent to the summit of non-figurative art is a difficult and agonizing climb, but satisfying nevertheless. At every step real things recede more and more into the distance, objects become merged into each other, until finally the world of ordinary ideas, in which, however, we live, fades out altogether. Away with the images of reality, away with ideal representations—nothing but the desert!

But this desert is full of the spirit of non-objective sensibility, which penetrates everywhere.

I, too, had a kind of timidity, and I hesitated to the point of anguish when I was about to abandon the ' world of will and representation ', in which I had lived and created, believing in its authenticity.

But the feeling of satisfaction which came with my liberation from the object took me still further into the desert, up to the point where nothing was authentic except sensibility—and so sensibility became the very substance of my life.

The picture that I had exhibited was not an empty picture, but sensibility in the absence of the object.

Painting is overtaken by time, and the painter is a prejudice of the past. "

Suprematist composition, painting 1915?

ument to the Resistance, at Udine.
lel by the architects Valle and Marco-
een from above.

ZO MARI

omatic experimental research with cubic
es.

CHINESE COINS

Chinese coins with square holes.

USELESS MACHINE

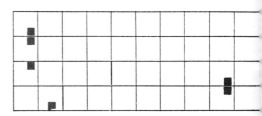

Harmonic sketch of the six elements which compose Munari's "Useless Machine 1956". The six elements (strips of natural anodized aluminium of various lengths) placed together on one level occupy the space of two and a half squares. Suspended on threads of nylon they can be arranged in infinite combinations.

MODULOR

Le Corbusier's modulor is a unit of measurement based on the human figure and on mathematics.

MONDRIAN

Composition with red, painting, 1936.

HALF

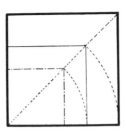

Given a square, describe one of half, and one of a quarter of its area.

NICAEA

The town of Nicaea in Bithynia (about 300 B.C.) was in the form of a square of about 700 meters a side, with two main streets which crossed at right angles and joined the four gates of the town.

MUSICAL NOTES

A line of music written in the eleventh century.

SPIRAL NEBULA

The logarithmic spiral is also found in the form of some nebulae.

PIER LUIGI and ANTONIO NERVI

The winning model in the competition for

the "Palace of Work" at Turin. The construction by Pier Luigi and Antonio Nervi involves a roof of sixteen independent square structures of 40 meters a side with a pillar for every 1,600 square meters of roof.

NEGATIVE POSITIVE

Pictorial composition without background in white, black and red. Munari, 1951.

NINTH ORDER

Magic square of the ninth order composed according to Bachet's rule.
The sum of the numbers in each vertical column or in each horizontal row is always the same.

77	28	69	20	61	12	53	4	45
36	68	19	60	11	52	3	44	76
67	27	59	10	51	2	43	75	35
26	58	18	50	1	42	74	34	66
57	17	49	9	41	73	33	65	25
16	48	8	40	81	32	64	24	56
47	7	39	80	31	72	23	55	15
6	38	79	30	71	22	63	14	46
37	78	29	70	21	62	13	54	5

NOTRE-DAME

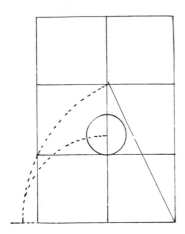

Scheme of the façade of Notre-Dame.

OPERA QUADRATA

An ancient system of masonry, found in Etruria and Latium, in which square blocks of marble or tufa were used.

COUNTRY

Japanese ideogram for " country ": an enclosure (the frontiers) contains a mouth (the people) and a bow (the army).

PAVILION

CM. 260 x 2 6

CM. 130 x 130

CM. 65 x 65

Textile Pavilion at the Eleventh Triennial Exhibition at Milan, by the architect Edoardo Sianesi. Plan and one of the four equal sides.

SQUARE PYRAMID

A square of cardboard with many alternating cuts, as shown in the illustration, suspended at the center, automatically forms this three-dimensional figure.

General plan of the Palace of the Achaemenidae at Persepolis (reconstruction).

PALLADIO

The use of the square in the architecture of Palladio is often the vital element in his buildings. The Villa Foscarini, near Stra, has a square ground-plan. Other square ar-chitectural areas are to be found in the Villa Thiene at Quinto Vicentino, in the Palazzo Iseppo de' Porti and in the Palazzo Thiene, both at Vicenza.

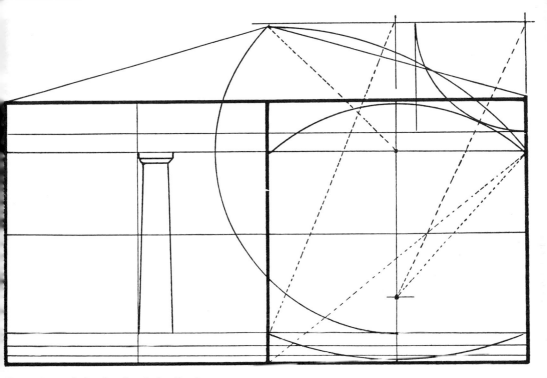

Proportions of the façade of the Parthenon.

PLATO

" We have divided the whole series of numbers into two classes: every number that can be formed by multiplying two equal factors we have represented in a figure with a square and we have called it a square and equilateral number. "

57

PALAZZO FARNESE

白い四角　　　JAPANESE POEM

のなか

の白い四角　　white square of
　　　　　　　inside the
のなか　　　　white square of
　　　　　　　inside the
の白い四角　　white square of
　　　　　　　inside the
のなか　　　　white square of
　　　　　　　inside the
の白い四角　　white square of
　　　　　　　inside the
のなか　　　　white square

の白い四角　　　Katué Kitasono

PROVERB

Who is born square will not die round.
Neapolitan proverb.

PURSE

Leather purse. It is closed by folding along
the diagonals of the vertical walls of the cube.

IRON PYRITES

The form of the cube in nature: cubic iron
pyrites from Elba.

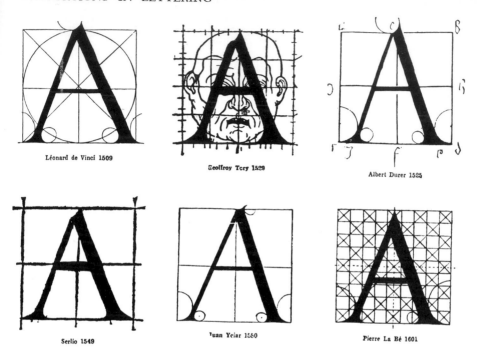

Léonard de Vinci 1509

Geoffroy Tory 1529

Albert Durer 1525

Serlio 1549

Juan Yciar 1550

Pierre La Bé 1601

Studies in proportions for the letters of the alphabet: Leonardo 1509, Geoffroy Tory 1529, Albrecht Dürer 1525, Serlio, 1549, Juan Yciar 1550, Pierre La Bé 1601.

PYTHAGORAS

Two illustrations of the Pythagorian theorem.

SQUARE - WINDOW

" A woman suffering from a brain disease, was incapable of copying a square, and it was evident that the figure meant nothing to her. On being asked what it was, she replied that it was something to do with a window. After many tests it became evident that she was only able to copy those models which to her looked like concrete objects. When she saw that she could not copy a model, because it had no meaning for her, she would sometimes modify it in such a way that it took on the characteristics of a concrete object; after which she was able to copy it.

Given a square, she produced the following:

When asked what these figures might mean, she replied, ' The windows of a church '. She did not draw squares without significance, but two windows of a church in a position in which one could really find them. Evidently where we see an abstract geometric figure the patient could only see a concrete object. "

MAGIC SQUARES

A magic square of the nth order is a square divided, like a chessboard, into n^2 smaller squares, or cells, where n is the number of cells in any side. Numbers are then inserted in the cells in such a way that the sum of the numbers in any line, horizontal or vertical, or in either of the two diagonals, is always the same. This sum is called the magic constant.

A magic square remains unaffected when subjected to any of the following changes, termed simple transformations:

a - rotation about the center through one, two or three right angles, clockwise or counterclockwise;

b - symmetrical reversal about the horizontal or vertical medians;

c - symmetrical reversal about either diagonal;

d - the substitution of every number with its complement in respect of $n^2 + 1$.

Eight magic squares of the third order:

4	3	8		6	7	2
9	5	1		1	5	9
2	7	6		8	3	4

3	9	4		8	1	6
7	5	3		3	5	7
6	1	8		4	9	2

2	7	6		4	9	2
9	5	1		3	5	7
4	3	8		8	1	6

8	3	4		6	1	8
1	5	9		7	5	3
6	7	2		2	9	4

Magic squares, which the old Indian mathematicians already knew how to construct, first became known in Europe in about 1420. In the Middle Ages they were believed to have supernatural powers and were worn as amulets against the evil eye, plague and other diseases. They had special meanings for astrologers: for Cornelius Agrippa the magic square of the first order symbolized unity and eternity; the impossibility of a magic square of the second order indicated the imperfection of the four elements (air, water, earth and fire); the seven magic squares of the third to the ninth orders represented the seven planets then known.

16	3	2	13
5	10	11	8
9	6	7	12
4	15	14	1

The following magic square of the fourth order is to be found in one of Albert Dürer's grotesques called "Melancholy", 1514, which year figures in the center of the bottom row.

Diego Palomino published a work on magic squares in Madrid, in 1599, without, however, giving any procedure for their construction. In 1612, C. G. Bachet published a method for constructing those of odd-numbered orders. De la Loubère published another method in 1691, called the border method. In 1693, P. H. De la Hire published a method for constructing squares of even-numbered orders, due to B. Frénicle, and gave all the 880 possible solutions for a magic square of the fourth order.

DIABOLIC SQUARES

Euler then constructed "panmagic" squares in which the sum of the numbers situated in every pair of complementary lines (meaning by that any pair of diagonal lines, one on either side of and parallel to the central diagonal, whose total numbers of cells is n), is also equal to the magic constant. The following square of the fourth order, for example, is panmagic:

1	12	7	14
8	13	2	11
10	3	16	5
15	6	9	4

Several studies on diabolic squares, as they were called by E. Lucas, A. H. Frost, M. Frolow and others, appeared between 1866 and 1886. Diabolic squares have the property of remaining magic when they are divided into two rectangles by any line parallel to the sides, the positions of which are then exchanged. The following is a diabolic square of the fourth order:

1	14	4	15
12	7	9	6
13	2	16	3
8	11	5	10

In 1849, E. Maillet published his researches on a general theory of magic squares based on the general theory of the substitution of n letters. G. Arnoux published "Les espaces arithmétiques hypermagiques" in Paris in 1894, where he evolved a very remarkable method for the construction of magic squares of the fourth order, a method later extended by A. Margossian in 1908 to the case of magic squares of any composite order.

SATANIC SQUARES

Interesting researches have, moreover, been published by A. Aubry in 1926 in "Sphinx-Oedipe". A magic square is termed bimagic if its numbers can be substituted by their squares; trimagic if they can also be substituted by their cubes. Such squares are also called satanic or cabbalistic.

MILITARY SQUARE

Ranks of soldiers drawn up in square formation.

MILITARY QUADRILATERAL

A quadrangular area of ground defended by four forts.

SQUARING THE CIRCLE

The most famous problem in the history of mathematics is the squaring of the circle. The first elements of geometry dealt with the possibilities of measuring a figure restricted to straight lines. In the Nile valley, where every year the floods obliterated any marks made by the farmers to indicate the bounds of their property, geometry helped to redefine them. Areas bounded by curved lines made difficulties in the calculations and it was sought to simplify the problem by defining the areas with straight lines only. If a square which had the same area as a circle could be constructed, by measuring the area of the square, one would also have that of the circle. The expression " squaring the circle " has its origin in this fact, but the difficulty of doing so was due to the nature of π.

SQUARE - TRIANGLE

A square, cut as shown and hinged at the points indicated, is transformed into an equilateral triangle by swinging the parts round on the level to their new positions.

FOUR POINTS IN SPACE

The four corner points are enough to give the impression of a square.

ANCIENT ROME

According to an ancient tradition, mentioned by some Greek authors, it seems that there was probably a Roma Quadrata distinct from that founded by Romulus, and older. From various historical sources and archeological discoveries, it appears that this Roma quadrata must have consisted of a square cell on the Palatine Hill in front of the Temple of Apollo, in which were preserved, before the city was founded, all the objects of good omen for its foundation, and which was closed with a square stone.

Hence the tradition of a Roma Quadrata older than that of Romulus: what was originally nothing a but a small cell gave its name to the whole new city, which was called Roma Quadrata or Roma Romulea indifferently.

ROTATION

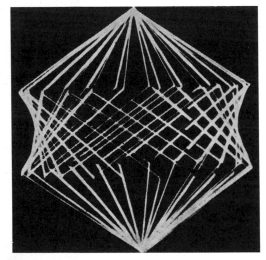

Figure derived from the rotation of a cube.

RENAISSANCE

Painted decoration.

RAMSES IV

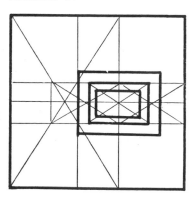

Proportional analysis of the plan of the tomb of Ramses IV.

RING

PROPORTIONAL RECTANGLES

Lowering the diagonal of a square onto the prolongation of the base, we get a rectangle in which, whatever the unit of measurement, the ratio between the sides is $1 : \sqrt{2}$. Continuing the process we get a series of rectangles with the following ratios: $1 : \sqrt{3}$, $1 : \sqrt{4}$ (i.e. an area of two squares, $1 : \sqrt{5}$, and so on.

CHESS IN MOSCOW

The opening of the Twelfth World Chess Championship in the Central Theatre of the Soviet Army in Moscow.

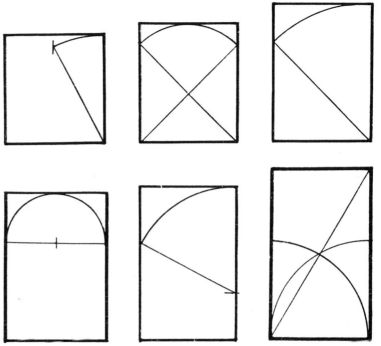

Rectangles obtained by the elongation of a square to various extents determined by certain of its own inherent measurements.

*Raphael. *The Marriage of the Virgin.*

WISDOM

The ancients represented Fortune seated on a round stone and Wisdom seated on a square stone, thereby showing that the former is fickle while the seat of the latter is firm and immovable.

PREHISTORIC SIGNS

Signs painted in blue-black and linear-red, of the most ancient series, found at Cachao da Rapa or Curral das Letras, Braganca. Similar signs are to be found also in paleo-Babylonian, northern Semitic and American proto-Indian writings.

THE KNIGHT'S TOUR

The problem of moving the knight through all sixty-four squares of the chessboard in sixty-three moves, known to the ancient Indian mathematicians, has a number of solutions not yet determined.
Euler and various other mathematicians indicated ways of solving the problem. Here are two solutions (the numbers denote the successive positions of the knight) of which

43	40	15	26	13	30	5	8
38	25	42	29	16	7	12	31
41	44	39	14	27	4	9	6
24	37	28	17	54	11	32	3
45	18	23	64	33	2	55	10
36	49	46	19	22	53	58	61
47	20	51	34	63	60	1	56
50	35	48	21	52	57	62	59

the second is " closed ", that is from the final position the knight can, in one move, return to his initial position:

BRUNO SERVI

The square represents number at its highest perfection, because, in its case, the number of times the base is repeated is also the number of times unity is repeated in the base.
In squaring, in fact, the mere enunciation of the base expresses in itself the number of times it is repeated; so that every external or arbitrary element is eliminated which, in the determination of the number of times of repetition, is always present in any other nonpotential operation.

ROCK-SALT

The square in nature: a crystal of rock-salt.

22	25	50	39	52	35	60	57
27	40	23	36	49	58	53	34
24	21	26	51	38	61	56	59
41	28	37	48	3	54	33	62
20	47	42	13	32	63	4	55
29	16	19	46	43	2	7	10
18	45	14	31	12	9	64	5
15	30	17	44	1	6	11	8

TRAFFIC SIGNS

Right of precedence; right of precedence ends.

LIBYAN CHARACTERS

Characters of Libyan writing.

SQUARE WRITING

Almost every country has a so-called square form for the letters of its alphabet or its ideograms. In Rome, the ancient capital letters used for monumental inscriptions were called " square ". Hebrew, Chinese and Japanese writing is square. Obviously a square form allows the best composition on a flat surface of vertical or horizontal texts.

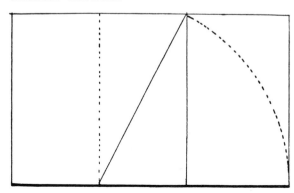

Characters of Balti writing, of the state of Kashmir, corresponding to the respective phonetic values: d, ts, b, h, k. Many characters of this writing, which is presumed to have been invented at the time of the conversion of the people to Islam around 1400, seem to have had, as their original basis, a square grid.
Such a grid probably gave an easily remembered form to each letter.

GOLDEN SECTION

Method of determining the golden section,

72

SQUARE DANCES

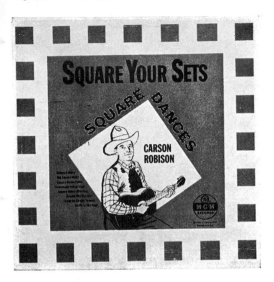

Instructions for the figures of square dances according to Carson Robison. Formation: four couples in one group. Form a square with a couple face to face on every side. A group should occupy a square space of nine feet per side. Every lady is on the right of her partner. The lady on the left of every gentleman is the corner lady. The principal couple, that is couple number one, dances back toward the part of the hall where the orchestra is. The couple on the right of the principal couple is couple number two, and so on for the third and fourth, or last couple.

Honor: the gentlemen bow, the ladies ends.

Swing: the gentleman takes the right hand of the lady on his left and puts his arm around her waist, as for a waltz. He places his right foot on the outside of the right foot of the lady and they dance around in a clockwise direction, spinning on the right foot.

Promenade: the couples cross hands and circle around the group in an counterclockwise direction.

Do-si-do: the lady and gentleman move towards each other and pass, right shoulder to right shoulder. Each takes a step to the right, passing back to back, and then both return to their original positions.

Allemande left: each gentleman faces towards his corner lady. They take each other by the left hand and wheel clockwise returning to their original positions. Grand right and left: the partners face each other and take each other by the right hand. They move towards each other and pass. The gentlemen spin counterclockwise and the ladies clockwise. Take the left hand of your neighbour, pass, and in this way proceed in a circle. Some titles of square dances: The Square Waltz, Square Dance Polka, Promenade Indian Style, Around the Outside, Birdie in the Cage.

RUNIC CHARACTERS

From a Runic alphabet, phonetic value: Oe, ae, e, o. The square has the phonetic value: ng.

THE LOGARITHMIC SPIRAL

From a square we can obtain a golden rectangle by lowering the diagonal between the center of the base and an opposite corner onto the prolongation of the base. If, to this rectangle, we attach another square based on the longer side we obtain another golden rectangle. Continuing attaching squares to the longer sides of the rectangles we obtain a figure composed of squares making a spiral form around the pole O, which is the point of intersection of the diagonals of the successive rectangles. If we draw a curve through the points of intersection of these diagonals with the successive squares, the curve will be a logarithmic spiral.

This curve represents the law of visible organic growth, especially in shells, in the arrangement of sunflower seeds, in some spiral nebulae and in many other cases.

Twelfth-century Scandinavian lock.

TATAMI

A tatami is a piece of thick matting with which the Japanese have been covering the floors of their houses for more than a thousand years. The tatami is two squares in size and serves as a basic unit of measurement in the building plan of a house. Every room is conceived on the basis of the number of tatami to be used, and it is sufficient to just state the number of tatami to be used in a room to get an idea of its shape and dimensions, and as every part of the house is based on the tatami formula, one may plan without having to make measurements.

FOSSIL SPONGE

Structure of a fossil sponge.

HITTITE CHARACTERS

Hittite characters. Part of a hieroglyph from inscriptions found at Hama, in Syria. The second character has the phonetic value: k, g.

SEAL

Sign from a proto-Indian seal.

EMPIRE STYLE

Detail of an Empire style balustrade.

ANTON STANKOWSKI

Poster design.

A square cut in this way may be recomposed in many other ways.

TETRAHEDRON

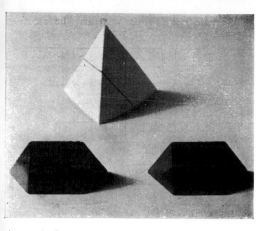

A tetrahedron may be cut into two identical pieces, the area of section being a square.

TELL EL AMARNA

A model village at Tell el Amarna (1370 B.C.) in which lived the workers and artisans employed on the construction of the tombs in the rock in the higher part of the desert. This village, situated in a desolate valley, far from water but near the cliffs where the tombs were to be cut out of the rock, was square in shape and surrounded by a high wall in which there was only one entrance. In the village itself there were five narrow streets which ran parallel from north to south, through lines of small, rentable houses, all identical in shape. Only in the south-east corner, near the gate, was there a bigger and more elaborate building, which was probably the house of the supervisor.

The monotony of all these houses was compensated for by the variety of what they contained. The men who worked in the tombs as painters and decorators used to bring home some of the colors, with the result that the walls of their houses were all decorated with rough designs. During the excavations, tools of every kind were found: clay crucibles, unworked precious stones, parts of looms, and rings with unfinished cut stones.

The well-protected houses in the city itself, of members of the court, seemed inhuman and without life in comparison with this humble workers' village.

TRIGON

A Swiss game composed of squares cut-up in such a way that different figures may be formed.

PASSAGGIO NORD

A

STRADA OCCIDENTALE

STRADA DEL LUNGO MURO

STRADA MAGGIORE

STRADA DELLA PORTA

STRADA ORIENTALE

PIAZZA SUD

ELL EL AMARNA

THE TEMPLE OF SOLOMON

The Temple of Solomon in Jerusalem. The Holy of Holies was a perfect square, with sides almost equal to that of Carchemish. It was completely bare, except for the front which was adorned with a curtain embroidered in various colors.

ONE QUARTER GREATER

Given a square, describe another one greater by a quarter.

A FIFTH

Given a square, describe another one fifth, two thirds, etc., smaller.

TETRAFLEX

Three-dimensional construction made with four squares fixed together at their parallel sides and having a cordon for every diagonal. This object may be folded in many ways always following the lines of the folds.

TWIDDLE

Cubic object cut in sixteen equal prismatic parts. These parts are hinged to each other in such a way as to allow its transformation into other parallelepipedal or prismatic objects, always keeping all the pieces attached to each other.

PHYSIOGNOMIC TYPES OF LEDOS

The square type indicates an energetic blunt nature, a firmness of character to the point of inflexibility, that may easily degenerate into stubbornness. An able reasoner, strictly and powerfully logical, with a well developed practical sense; having a propensity for the exact sciences, for philosophy and mathematics, but lacking in imagination, which allows little aptitude for the arts. A lover of construction, he has the mental attitude of the architect. His nature, sceptical and doubting, leads him to materialism; if faith illuminates his soul it will rest on unshakeable foundations; the head will always control the heart. This type generally lives long.

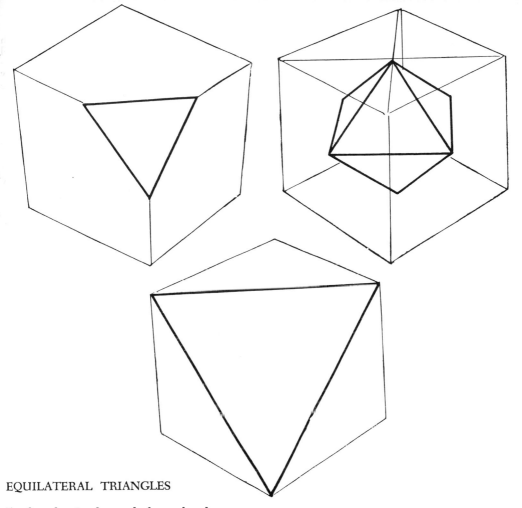

EQUILATERAL TRIANGLES

Equilateral triangles and forms based on
equilateral triangles in cubic spaces.

UO

Mayan character; phonetic value: uo.

$1 \times 5 - 2 \times 2.$

Apparent transformation of a rectangle 1×5 into a square 2×2.

URANIUM AND GRAPHITE

A large cube of uranium and graphite for the first nuclear reactor.

VASARELY

Detail of a large composition in black and white.

MIES VAN DER ROHE

Plan and front elevation of the " 50 × 50 "

MARY VIEIRA

From square to cube. Form in stainless steel 35 × 35 × 35 cm. Basle, 1959. Collection of Dr. Markus Kutter, Basle.

WANG HSI-CHIH

Wang Hsi-Chih, who lived in the time of the Eastern Chin dynasty (A.D. 316-420), is considered the true father of Chinese calligraphy. He perfected the " li ssu " characters by giving them their beautiful square form, as well as the script which nowadays we call cursive, still undeveloped in his time, and he invented an intermediary form between the two. The present-day Chinese characters therefore belong to one or other of the three forms he established: squared, medium and cursive. To him is due the merit for having perfected them in such a highly artistic and admirable manner.

一面一面的比較話句子跟圖,就明白話句子的意思了。不用太使勁記,只要留心話句子怎麼變意思怎麼跟着變就成了。這麼樣學英國話,不大像用功,倒很像遊戲。

　用這本書的時候,越把中國話忘掉越好,圖就會把意思告訴你了。在這會兒把英國話翻成中國話,只有學起來更困難的。有一套留聲機片把書上的話說給你聽,說一句歇一歇,爲是你好跟着說。如果你自己用功,沒有這套留聲機片,頂好先學認字用字,等有了幫手再學念學說。每次兩三面一塊兒練習直到背得出圖上的話句子爲止。造句子的時候別淨靠死記;想法兒用英國話體

INDEX

As all the subjects in this book have been arranged in alphabetical order (as far as make-up allows) no index is necessary.

English translation by Desmond O' Grady.

Bibliography:

Maurice Kraitchik LA MATHÈMATIQUE DES JEUX
BAUHAUS The Museum of Modern Art, New York.
Marcel Poëte LA CITTÀ ANTICA
Diringer L'ALFABETO NELLA STORIA DELLA CIVILTÀ
Drexler THE ARCHITECTURE OF JAPAN The Museum of Modern Art, New York.
Ernst Mössel VOM GEHEIMNIS DER FORM UND DER URFORM DES SEINS, Stuttgart
Gyorgy Kepes LANGUAGE OF VISION Theobald, Chicago.
Gyorgy Kepes THE NEW LANDSCAPE Theobald, Chicago.
Karl Gerstner KALTE KUNST? Niggli, Teufen AR,
Wolfgang von Wersin DAS BUCH VOM RECHTECK Maier, Ravensburg.
Steinhaus MATHEMATICAL SNAPSHOTS Oxford University Press, New York.
David Katz LA PSICOLOGIA DELLA FORMA
G. Ronchetti DIZIONARIO ILLUSTRATO DEI SIMBOLI
Karnes and Newman MATEMATICA E IMMAGINAZIONE
ENCICLOPEDIA DELLE MATEMATICHE ELEMENTARI
Pio Emanuelli IL CIELO E LE SUE MERAVIGLIE
Umberto Forti GEOMETRIA PIANA
Leonard Wolley IL MESTIERE DELL'ARCHEOLOGO
DE STIJL Stedelijk Museum, Amsterdam.
KONKRETE KUNST Kunsthalle, Basel.
ARTE ASTRATTA E CONCRETA
AUJOURD'HUI, Paris, n. 3-4-9.
CIVILTÀ DELLE MACCHINE,
SCIENTIFIC AMERICAN, New York, May 1958, November 1958.
ILLUSTRAZIONE SCIENTIFICA,
ART, Paris.
ENCICLOPEDIA DELLA CIVILTÀ ATOMICA,
Boris de Rachewiltz INCONTRO CON L'ARTE EGIZIANA,
Henry Poincaré LA SCIENCE ET L'HIPOTHÈSE.
Luigi Dami I GIARDINI ITALIANI
Hornung's Handbook of DESIGN and DEVICES Dover Publication, New York.
Cesare Bairati LA SIMMETRIA DINAMICA
A. Speltz LES STYLES DE L'ORNEMENT
Gardner Murphy SOMMARIO DI PSICOLOGIA
Egmont Colerus IL ROMANZO DELLA GEOMETRIA
Zevi POETICA DELL'ARCHITETTURA NEOPLASTICA

Other Books published or distributed by George Wittenborn, Inc.

1018 Madison Avenue, New York, N. Y. 10021
and 91 Montgomery Street, Scarsdale, N. Y. 10583

Aalto (Alvar) Complete Works 1922-1960. over 600 ill. 1963 $18.50
Albers (Josef) Poems and Drawings. 22 ill. rev. ed. 1961 $7.50
Alloway (Lawrence) Ettore Colla, Iron Sculpture. 28 ill. 1960 $8.50
Alvard (Julien and S. Lupasco) Frederic Benrath. 10 ill. 1959 $2.50
American Abstract Artists 1936-1966. Contributions by Albers, Bolotowsky, Kelpe, Lassaw, Mason, Morris, Shaw, Slobodkina and others, ill. 1966 $4.50
American Abstract Artists (Editors) *The World of Abstract Art.* 162 ill. 1957 $8.50
Annual of Architecture, Structure and Townplanning,
      Vol. 3 Ed. by the Association of Architects, Engineers and Townplanners, India, Honorary editor: Santosh Ghosh. 150 ill. 1963 $9.50
      Vol. 4 400 ill. 1964 $9.50
      Vol. 5 in preparation, ready 1967
Architecture: Formes & Fonctions. Ed. by Anthony Krafft
      Vol. 9 1962-1963 250 p., ill., $9.50
      Vol. 10 1963-1964 240 p., ill. $10.00
      Vol. 11 1964-1965. 291 pp., ill. $11.00
      Vol. 12 1965-1966. 238 pp., ill. $11.00
Art de France, Ed. by Andre Chastel
      Vol. 1 488 pp., 500 ill. 1960 $17.50
Atchley (Dana) *ABC Design.* 32 silk-screened p., acetate stencil, limited ed. 1965 $9.00
Atelier 17, Hayter Print Group. 23 ill. 1949 $3.50
Baljeu (Joost) *Attempt at a Theory of Synthesist Plastic Expression.* 14 ill. 1964 $2.00
Barrett (Douglas) *Early Cola Bronzes (850-1014 A.D.)* 102 ill., 1965 $13.50
Baumann (Ernst) *New Gardens.* 500 ill. 1955 $11.50
Beckmann, Max Beckmann, ed. by J. B. Neumann and G. Franke, 48 ill. (Vol. 5 in the Art Lover Library), 1931 $1.50
Berne (Stanley) *The Dialogues.* 14 surrealist ill by Matta, limited ed. 1962 $5.00
        The Multiple Modern Gods and Other Stories. 8 woodcuts by Herman Zaage. 1964 $5.00
Blaser (Werner) *Structure and Form in Japan.* 205 ill. 1963 $15.00
Bolaffi's Catalogue of Modern Art 1966. 2000 ill. 1966 $40.00
Bosquet (Alain) *La Peinture de Dorothea Tanning.* 115 ill. 1966 $9.00
Brancusi: His Early Works: 1905-1908, by Geo. Bogza, ill. 1965 $10.00

Brandi (Cesare) *Burri*. 134 ill., folio, boxed 1964 $40.00

Branner (Robert) *La Cathedrale de Bourges et sa Place dans l'Architecture Gothique*. 138 ill. 1962 $10.00.

Brenson (Theodore) *Light into Color, Light into Space*. 15 ill. 1959 $2.50

Brongers (Georg A.) *Nicotiana Tabacum. The History of Tobacco Smoking in the Netherlands*. 167 ill., some in color, bibliog., 1964 $12.50

Bufano (Beniamino) *American Sculptor*. vol. 1 122 ill. 1957 $17.50
   vol. 2 in preparation, ready end of 1967

Bullrich (Francisco) *Arquitectura Argentina Contemporanea*. 300 ill. 1964 $7.00

(Le) Cabinet Fantastique
   Vol. 1: *Projets et Divagations de C. N. Ledoux, Architecte du Roi*, French text by Y. Christ. 80 ill. 1961 $10.00
   Vol. 2: *Didier Barra et Francois de Nome dits, Monsu Desiderio*, French text by Dr. Felix Sluys. 114 ill. 1961 $12.50
   Vol. 3: *Victor Hugo Dessinateur*, by Gaetan Picon. 250 ill. 1964 $15.00
   Vol. 4: *Bresdin*, by Claude Roger-Marx. 264 ill., 1966 $15.00

Callery (Mary) *Sculpture*. 172 ill. 1961 $15.00

Campigli (Massimo) *Scrupules*. 117 ill. 1957 $9.50

Carli (Enzo) *Il Duomo di Orvieto*. 267 ill. 1965 $67.50

Carver (Norman F.) *Silent Cities of Mexico and the Maya*. 170 ill., 16 drawings, 1965 $20.00

Ceroni (Ambrogio) *Modigliani: Dessins, Sculptures*. 222 ill. 1965 $15.00

Chermayeff (Ivan) *Blind Mice and Other Numbers*. over 50 ill. 1961 $3.50

Cirlot (Juan-Eduardo) *Lucio Fontana*. 37 ill. 1966 $4.00

Coburn (Alvin Langdon) *A Portfolio*. 16 ill. limited ed. 1962 $12.50

Cossio del Pomar (Felipe) *Peruvian Colonial Art: The Cuzco School of Painting*. 65 ill. 18 color plates, 1965 $10.00

Crispolti (E. and G. Marchiori) *Corrado Cagli*. 268 ill., 88 color plates, 1964 $37.50

Cuevas by Cuevas. 100 ill. 1965 $5.00

(The) Dada Movement (Galleria Schwarz, Milan)
   1. *Arman, Raysse, Spoerri, Dufrene, Rotelfo, Villegle*. 94 ill. 1966 $1.50
   2. *Dada in Italy*. in prep. 1966 $1.50
   3. *'Round the World with Dada*. in prep. 1966 $1.50
   4. *The Protagonists: Dada is 50 Years Young*. in prep. 1966 $1.50
   5. *Towards a Cold Poetic Image*. in prep. 1966 $1.50

De Angelis D'Ossat (G. and C. Pietrangeli) *Il Campidoglio di Michelangelo*. 49 ill., over 100 drawings, plans, 1965 $95.00

De Bock (Paul Aloise) *Paul Delvaux: Der Mensch, Der Maler*. 56 ill. 1965 $8.50

Other Books published or distributed by George Wittenborn, Inc.

1018 Madison Avenue, New York, N. Y. 10021
and 91 Montgomery Street, Scarsdale, N. Y. 10583

Degas (Edgar) *Huit Sonnets*. 19 ill. 1947 $4.00
Denby (Edwin) *Mediterranean Cities*. 30 ill. 1956 $7.50
Dereux (Philippe) *Raymond Grandjean*. 10 ill. 1959 $2.50
Deroudille (Rene) *Rene Laubies*. French text 10 ill. 1957 $3.00
Documenti D'Arte D'Oggi, Ed. by the mac espace group in Milan, Italy
        Vol. 3 1955-1956, 110 ill. $12.50
        Vol. 4 1956-1957, 160 ill. $12.50
        Vol. 5 1957-1958, 100 ill. $12.50
Documents of Modern Art Series. See: Cover page
Dooijes (D. and P. Brattinga) *History of the Dutch Poster*. 350 ill. 1966 c. $28.00
Due Dimensioni. A dictionary of contemporary Italian commercial designers, text in 4 languages,
        edited by Max Huber et al, 2700 ill. 1965 $30.00
Duthuit (Georges) *Le Serpent dans la Galere*. 34 ill. 1945 $15.00
Far Eastern Antiquities Museum, Stockholm. Details on request
        Bulletin No. 36, 250 pp., 75 ill. 1964 $14.75
        Bulletin No. 37, 254 pp., 81 ill. 1965 $14.75
(Le) Fauconnier. Text by Ozenfant, ed. by J. B. Neumann, 9 ill. 1949 $1.00
Feldman (Eugene) *New York: West Side*. Fold-out plate in end boards, limited ed. 1965 $50.00
Focillon (Henri *The Life of Forms In Art*. 19 ill. reprint 1966 $2.50
Four Great Makers of Modern Architecture. Gropius, Le Corbusier, Mies van der Rohe, Wright. Sym-
        posium held at Columbia University School of Architecture in 1961. 1964 $7.50
Gallatin (A. E.) *Paintings of A. E. Gallatin*. 40 ill. 1948 $2.50
Gangoly (O. C.) *Indian Terracotta Art*. 50 ill. 1959 $9.00
Gasparini (Graziano)
        La Arquitectura Colonial de Coro. ill. 1961 $20.00
        La Arquitectura Colonial en Venezuela. ill. 1965 $30.00
        La Casa Colonial Venezolana. 147 ill. 1962 $7.50
Gaudi (Antonio) Preface by Le Corbusier. 61 ill. 1958 $7.50
George (Waldemar) *Hilaire Hiler and Structuralism: New Concept of Form-Color*. 8 ill. 1958 $2.50
Gindertall (R. V.) *Morice Lipsi*. 104 ill. 1965/ $15.00
Gleizes (Albert) *Le Cubisme 1908-1914. Cahiers*. Vol. 1 : Souvenirs. ill. 1957 $3.00
Goeritz. *Mathias Goeritz*, by Olivia Zuniga. 190 ill. 1963 $7.00

Green (Samuel Adams) *Andy Warhol*. 27 ill. 1965 $7.50

Gregory (Albert) *Color in Line*. 16 ill., limited ed. 1960 $40.00

Haass (Terry and Ferrand, Michel) *Germinal*. 6 orig. color etchings. 1957 $100.00

Hammer (Victor) *Memory and Her Nine Daughters*. 1957 $15.00

Henze (Anton) *La Tourette: The Le Corbusier Monastery*. 48 photos by B. Moosbrugger, 1966 $4.50

Herzka (Dorothy) *Pop Art*. 27 ill. 1965 $3.00

Honegger (Gottfried) *Fiktion und Realität erster Versuch einer Zusammenfassung meines heutigen Stand-
ortes in 24 Texten*. 5 orig. lithographs. 1956 $25.00

Honegger-Lavater (Warja) Folded stories. Original lithographs in numbered editions.

    2. *Die Grille und die Ameise* (The Grasshopper and the Ant) $3.50

    3. *Match* $3.50

    4. *Die Party* $3.50

    5. *La Promenade en Ville* $3.50

    6. *Rape of the Sabines* $3.75

    7. *Passion and Reason* $3.75

    8. *The Good Intention is Blue* $4.50

    9. *Night and Day and Night . . . and Day and Night* $4.50

   10. *Extra-ordinary Lemuel* $4.50

Hostettler (Rudolf) *Technical Terms of the Printing Industry*. 3rd rev. ed. 200 ill. 1959 $4.00

Howarth (Thomas) *Charles Rennie Mackintosh and the Modern Movement*. 250 ill. 1953 $12.50

Ioannou (A. S.) *Byzantine Frescoes of Euboea*. Vol. 1 100 ill. 1959 $10.00

Jenkins (Paul) *Seeing Voice, Welsh Heart*. 17 poems by Cyril Hodges, 6 original color lithos, limited
ed., 1965 $150.00

Kahn (Louis I.) *The Notebooks and Drawings of Louis I. Kahn*. over 100 ill. 1962 $14.50

Kahnweiler (D. H.) *Pour Daniel-Henry Kahnweiler*. 42 ill., 8 color lithos by Mourlot, 1965 $35.00

Kent (Adaline) *Autobiography*. 78 ill. 1958 $5.00

Kinetic Art. Four essays by Stephen Bann, Reg Gadney, Frank Popper and Philip Steadman. 80 ill.
1966 $3.00

Le Corbusier Complete Works. 1910-1960 800 ill. reprint ready 1967

        Vol. 1: 1910-1929, 400 ill. 1960 $15.00

        Vol. 2: 1929-1934, 400 ill. 1964 $15.00

        Vol. 3: 1934-1938, 400 ill. 1964 $15.00

        Vol. 4: 1938-1946, 400 ill. 1961 $15.00

        Vol. 5: 1946-1952, 400 ill. 1955 $15.00

        Vol. 6: 1952-1957, 500 ill. 1957 $15.00

        Vol. 7: 1957-1962, 500 ill. 1965 $18.50

Other Books published or distributed by George Wittenborn, Inc.

1018 Madison Avenue, New York, N. Y. 10021
and 91 Montgomery Street, Scarsdale, N. Y. 10583

Lehmbruck. *Die Druckgraphik von Wilhelm Lehmbruck*, by Erwin Petermann. 239 ill. 1964 $45.00
(Louise) Leiris Gallery Exhibition Catalogues, ill.
Series A:
    1. *Pablo Picasso: Peintures, 1955-1956* $3.50
    2. *Andre Masson: Peintures recentes et anciennes* $4.50
    3. *A Beaudin: Peintures, 1927-1957* $2.50
    4. *Juan Gris: Peintures de 1926 et 1927* $4.50
    5. *E. de Kermadec: Peintures 1927-56* $4.50
    6. *Fernand Leger: Dessins et Gouaches* $4.50
    7. *Suzanne Roger: Peintures 1923-1958* $2.50
    8. *Henri Laurens: Sculptures en pierre* $2.50
    9. *Elie Lascaux: Peintures 1921-1959* $4.50
    10. *Picasso: Les Menines 1957* $4.50
    11. *Picasso: 45 gravures sur linoleum, 1958-1960* $4.50
    12. *Picasso: Dessins 1959-1960* $3.50
    13. *Y. Rouvre: Peintures 1951-1961* $2.50
    14. *Picasso: Peintures (Vauvenargues 1959-1961)* $4.50
    15. *A. Masson: Peintures 1960-1961* $4.50
    16. *Picasso: "Dejeuner sur l'Herbe" de Manet* $4.50
    17. *Picasso: Peintures 1962-1963* (now out of print)
Series B:
    1. *D.-H. Kahnweiler: 50 Ans d'Edition* $3.50
    2. *A. Masson: Dessins, 1960* $2.50
    3. *Manolo: Sculptures-Gouaches-Dessins* $4.50
    5. *Juan Gris: Dessins* $4.50
    6 *Henri Laurens: Terre-Cuites (Clay Sculptures)* $2.50
    7. *A. Beaudin: Sculptures* $2.50
Lewis (David) Mondrian. *His Paintings.* 10 ill. 1957 $2.50
    Constantin Brancusi. 65 ill. 1958 $3.50
Leymarie (Jean) *Marc Chagall Monotypes, 1961-1965.* 25 color ill., limited ed. 1966 $42.50
Macagy (Douglas) *James Boynton.* 14 ill. 1959 $3.95
Madsen (Stephan Tschudi) *Munch's Wall Paintings.* 13 ill. 1959 $1.00

Maechler (Rene and Georges Thonet) *Paesaggi di Donna*. 35 photographs of the nude, 1965 $12.50

Marchiori (Giuseppe) *Jean Arp 1913-1963*. 95 ill. 1963 $20.00

Marchiori (Giuseppe) *Quinto Ghermandi*. 45 ill. 1962 $4.50

Masson (Andre) *Mythology of Being*. limited ed. 9 ill. portfolio. 1942 $25.00

        Nocturnal Notebook 16 ill. 1944 $3.00

Mathieu (Georges) *From the Abstract to The Possible*. 21 ill. 1960 $3.50

Medieval Wooden Sculpture in Sweden

    Vol. 1: *Attitudes to the Heritage*. ill. 1964 $8.50

    Vol. 2: *Romanesque and Gothic Sculpture*. ill. 1966 $9.50

    Vol. 3: *Late Medieval Sculpture*. ill. 1966 $9.50

    Vol. 4: *Catalogue*. ill. 1966 $17.50

    Vol. 5: *Plates*. 1964 $35.00

Mercandino (Cesare) *Impianti Sportivi*. 2 vols., ill. 1965 $40.00

Miranda (Salvador) *Les Palais des Empereurs Byzantins*. 34 ill., limited ed. 1965 $10.00

Modern Artists In America, Ed. by R. Motherwell, Ad Reinhardt, B. Karpel. 160 ill. 1952 $8.50

Monet (Claude) by Adrian Stokes, 8 color plates. 1958 $2.50

Moore (Henry) *Sculpture & Drawings*:

    Vol. 1. 1921-1948. 254 ill. 1957 $15.00

    Vol. 2. 1949-1954. 195 ill. reprint, 1965 $15.00

    Vol. 3. 1955-1964. 148 ill. 1965 $15.00

        Stone and Wood Carvings 1922-1961. 57 ill. 1961 $4.00

Moscanyi (Paul) *Karl Knaths*. 60 ill. 1958 $5.00

Mroszczak (Jozef) *Polnische Plakatkunst* (The Polish Poster In Art) 377 ill. 1962 $16.50

Muehsam (Alice) *German Readings 2: A Brief survey of art from the middle ages to the twentieth century for students of German and fine arts*. 2nd rev. ed. 1965 $3.50

Munari (Bruno) *The Circle*. ill. 1966 $4.50

      The Square. ill. reprint 1966 $4.50

      Good Design. ill. 1964 $1.50

New Furniture

    Vol. 4: 1956-1958. 347 ill. 1958 $12.50

Novelli (Gastone) *Antologia del Possible*. ill. 1962 $4.00

Of Art, Plato To Picasso. Ed. by A. E. Gallatin. 3 ill. 1963 $2.00

Otto (Frei) *Zugbeanspruchte Konstruktionen* (Shell Constructions)

    Vol. 1: *Pneumatische Konstruktionen Berechnung der Membranen, Zugverankerungen im Baugrund*. ill. 1962 $38.50

Other Books published or distributed by George Wittenborn, Inc.

1018 Madison Avenue, New York, N. Y. 10021
and 91 Montgomery Street, Scarsdale, N. Y. 10583

Vol. 2: *Grundbegriffe und Uebersicht der Konstrucktionen, Berechnung von Seilen, Seilnetzen und Seilwerken.* ill. 1966 $25.00

Vol. 3: *Spannweiten, Ideen und Versuche zum Leichtbau.* Ein Werkstattbericht von Conrad Roland. ill. 1965 $15.00

Picasso (Pablo) *Guernica.* 33 ill. 1956 $1.50

Lithographs 1945-1948. 67 ill. 1948 $3.00

Pirelli (Giulia and Carlo Orsi) *Milano.* 54 photos. 1965 $15.00

Ponente (Nello) *Mastroianni.* ill., limited ed., 1963 $27.50

(Les) Primitifs Flamands

Vol. 4: *New England Museums,* by Colin T. Eisler. ill. 1961 $13.50

Vol. 5: *Le Musee National de Louvre,* by Helene Adhemar. ill. 1962 $15.50

Vol. 6: *La Chapelle Royale de Grenada,* by Roger von Schoute. ill. 1963 $18.50

Vol. 7: *Le Palais Ducal D'Urbin,* by Jacques Lavalleye. ill. 1964 $20.00

Vol. 8: *Le Musee de l'Ermitage,* by Vladimir Loewinson-Lessing and Nicolas Nicouline. ill. 1965 $17.50

Vol. 9: *Les Musees de Pologne.* in prep. 1966

Problems of Contemporary Art Series. See: Cover page

Rand (Paul) *Trademarks.* 1960 $10.00

Thoughts On Design. 94 ill. $15.00

Read (Herbert) *Kandinsky 1866-1944.* 8 ill. 1959 $2.50

Redig de Campos (D.) *Raffaello Nelle Stanze.* 73 color plates, 1965 $45.00

Rety (Louis) *Fely Mouttet, Peintre.* 12 ill. 1958 $2.00

Reynal (Jeanne) *The Mosaics of Jeanne Reynal.* 81 ill. 1964 $15.00

Richter (Hans and Herbert Read) *Hans Richter.* 144 ill. 1965 $19.50

Rodin, Auguste) *A la Venus de Milo.* Fr. text. 6 ill. 1945 $4.00

Roesch (Kurt) 9 Engravings to accompany "The Sonnets to Orpheus" by Rainer Maria Rilke. 35 numbered and signed copies. 1944 $250.00

Rosenthal (Erwin) *The Changing Concept of Reality in Art.* 46 ill. 1962 $6.50

Ruscha (Edward) *Twenty Six Gasoline Stations.* 26 photos, 1962 $3.00

Various Small Fires. 20 photos, 1964 $3.00

Some Los Angelos Apartments. 40 photos of exteriors, 1965 $3.00

Sauvage (Tristan) *Nuclear Art.* Essays, manifestoes, 213 ill. 1962 $17.50

Schoofs (Rudolf) *Engravings*. Vol. 1. 22 ill. 1960 $2.50
                   Engravings. Vol. 2. 16 ill. 1963 $4.50
Seuphor (Michel) *Lee Hersch, Abstract Artist*. 12 ill. 1954 $2.50
Shorr (Dorothy C.) *The Christ Child in Devotional Images In Italy during the 14th Century*. 450 ill. 1953 $6.50
Stahly (Francois) *Francois Stahly*. 84 ill. 1962 $6.50
Steinberg (Leo) *Jasper Johns. A critical study*. 30 ill. 1963 $3.50
Sweeney (James Johnson) *Afro (Basaldella) Paintings, Gouaches, Drawings*. 34 ill. 1961 $20.00
            The Miro Atmosphere. 93 ill. 1959 $7.50
        Same, with one signed orig. color litho. $75.00
Taillandier (Yvon) *Creation Miro 1961*. 60 ill. 1962 $9.00
Tanguy (Yves) *Catalogue of the Paintings of Yves Tanguy*. 462 ill. 1963 $37.50
Tapie (Michel) *Antonio Tapies*. 46 photographs. 1959 $7.50
Tapies. *Antoni Tapies*, by Blai Bonet. Spanish text, ill. 1965 $54.50
               Observations. 8 ill. 1956 $3.50
               Claire Falkenstein. 19 ill. 1959 $5.50
Teshigahara (Sofu) *Portfolio*. 31 ill. $9.00
               Sculpture, 1957-58. 27 ill. $6.00
Trans/Formation: arts, communication, environment, Ed. by H. Holtzman
      Vol. 1, No. 1 1950 $3.50
      Vol. 1, No. 2 1951 $3.50
      Vol. 1, No. 3 1952 $3.50
Trucchi (Lorenzo) *Jean Dubuffet*. Italian text, 360 ill. 1965 $45.00
Tselos (Dimitri) *The Sources of the Utrecht Psalter Miniatures*. 361 ill. 1960 $20.00
Vasarely. *Victor Vasarely*, by Victor and Marcel Joray. ill. 1965 $27.50
Villani (D.) *Storia del Manifesto Pubblicitario*. History of the Poster. 900 ill. 1965 $36.00
Werbeform (German Graphic Annual).
      Vol. 3:   German-Eng. text, 1000 ill. 1962 $20.00
Weston (Edward) *The Daybooks of Edward Weston*. Vol. 1: Mexico. 40 ill. 1962 $10.00
Wilke (Ulfert) *One, Two and More*. portfolio, limited ed. 1960 $20.00
               Fragments from Nowhere. 19 facsimiles. 1960 $20.00
Wurman (Richard Saul) *Various Dwellings Described in a Comparative Manner*. 35 drawings by students of University of North Carolina School of Design, 1964 $7.00
Young (Dennis and Barbara) *Furniture in Britain Today*. 310 ill. 1964 $10.50
Zannas (Eliky) *Khajuraho*. 176 ill. 1961 $47.50
Zekowski (Arlene) *Concretions*. 13 ill. by Milton Avery, limited edition. 1962 $5.00
               Abraxas. 8 woodcuts by Herman Zaage, 1964 $5.00